Kate came to stay.

Mum and Kate made a cake.

Kate put little eggs on it.

Wilma looked at the little eggs.

She had an idea.

Wilma went to the park.

She wanted to hide some eggs.

She put them in the trees.

She put them in the flowers.

Wilf and Kate came to the park.

"You can look for eggs," said
Wilma.

Kate looked for the eggs.

"Where are they?" she said.

The squirrels had them.

"Squirrels like eggs," said Kate.

"So do I," she said.